C000136122

STAR MATHS STARTERS

A fresh approach to mental maths

TERMS AND CONDITIONS

IMPORTANT - PERMITTED USE AND WARNINGS - READ CAREFULLY BEFORE USING

Minimum specification:
- PC with a CD-ROM drive and 512 Mb RAM (recommended)
- Windows 98SE or above/Mac OSX.1 or above
- Recommended minimum processor speed: 1 GHz
- Facilities for printing

Julie Cogill and Anthony David

Authors
Julie Cogill and Anthony David

Anthony David dedicates this book to his wife Peachey, and sons Oliver and Samuel.

Editors
Niamh O'Carroll and Carolyn Richardson

Assistant Editors
Ruth Burns and Margaret Eaton

Illustrator
Theresa Tibbetts (Beehive Illustration)

Series Designer
Joy Monkhouse

Designers
Rebecca Male and Melissa Leeke

Text © Julie Cogill and Anthony David
© 2008 Scholastic Ltd

CD-ROM development in association with Vivid Interactive

Designed using Adobe InDesign and Adobe Illustrator

Published by Scholastic Ltd
Villiers House, Clarendon Avenue,
Leamington Spa, Warwickshire CV32 5PR
www.scholastic.co.uk

Printed by Tien Wah, Singapore
1 2 3 4 5 6 7 8 9   8 9 0 1 2 3 4 5 6 7

ISBN 978-1407-10008-1

ACKNOWLEDGEMENTS
Extracts from the Primary National Strategy's *Primary Framework for Mathematics* (2006)
www.standards.dfes.gov.uk/primaryframework, *Renewing the Primary Framework* (2006) and the
Interactive Teaching Programs originally developed for the National Numeracy Strategy © Crown
copyright. Reproduced under the terms of the Click Use Licence.

Every effort has been made to trace copyright holders for the works reproduced in this book, and the
publishers apologise for any inadvertent omissions.

British Library Cataloguing-in-Publication Data
A catalogue record for this book is available from the British Library.

Introduction

Introduction..4

The six Rs...7

Whiteboard hints and tips....................................8

Objectives grid...10

Planning for the six Rs..12

Activities

Shopping: money problems...13
Targets: number sentences...14
Find the cat: follow instructions..................................15
Dominoes: numbers to 20..16
Counting on and back (ITP)...17
Place value (ITP)...18
Twenty cards (ITP): order numbers.............................19
Bricks: order numbers to 100.......................................20
Fractions of shapes..21
Number spinners (ITP): addition and subtraction...22
Bingo: addition and subtraction..................................23
Halving and doubling to 20...24
Bingo: multiply by 2, 5 and 10....................................25
Multiplication square: 2-, 5- and 10-times tables...26
Function machine: multiply by 2, 5 or 10.................27
Maths Boggle: addition..28
Beanstalk: addition and subtraction..........................29
Maths Boggle: addition and subtraction....................30
Function machine: addition and subtraction............31
Number line (ITP): addition and subtraction...........32
Find the missing number: addition and subtraction...33
Find the missing number: multiplication and division...34
Dominoes: names of shapes...35
Reflection patterns...36
Maps and directions...37
Weighing scales: standard units.................................38
Measuring jug: read a scale...39
Fixing points (ITP): using a ruler................................40
Clocks: read the time...41
Block graph: favourite fruit..42

Photocopiable templates

Targets..43
Bingo...44
Beanstalk...45
Maps and directions...46

Star Maths Starters diary....................................47

Introduction

In the 1999 *Framework for Teaching Mathematics* the first part of the daily mathematics lesson is described as 'whole-class work to rehearse, sharpen and develop mental and oral skills'. The Framework identified a number of short, focused activities that might form part of this oral and mental work. Teachers responded very positively to these 'starters' and they were often judged by Ofsted to be the strongest part of mathematics lessons.

However, the renewed *Primary Framework for Mathematics* (2006) highlights that the initial focus of 'starters', as rehearsing mental and oral skills, has expanded to become a vehicle for teaching a range of mathematics. 'Too often the "starter" has become an activity extended beyond the recommended five to ten minutes' (*Renewing the Primary Framework for mathematics: Guidance paper,* 2006). The renewed Framework also suggests that 'the focus on oral and mental calculation has been lost and needs to be reinvigorated'.

Star Maths Starters aims to 'freshen up' the oral and mental starter by providing focused activities that help to secure children's knowledge and sharpen their oral and mental skills. It is a new series, designed to provide classes and teachers with a bank of stimulating interactive whiteboard resources for use as starter activities. Each of the 30 starters offers a short, focused activity designed for the first five to ten minutes of the daily mathematics lesson. Equally, the starters can be used as stand-alone oral and mental maths 'games' to get the most from a spare ten minutes in the day.

About the book

Each book includes a bank of teachers' notes linked to the interactive whole-class activities on the CD-ROM. A range of additional support is also provided, including planning grids, classroom resources, generic support for using the interactive whiteboard in mathematics lessons, and an objectives grid.

Objectives grid

A comprehensive two-page planning grid identifies links to the *Primary Framework for Mathematics* strands and objectives. The grid also identifies one of six starter types, appropriate to each interactive activity (see page 7 for further information).

Starter Number	Star Starter Title	Page No.	Strand	Learning objective as taken from the Primary Framework for Mathematics	Type of Starter
1	Shopping: money problems	13	Using and applying mathematics	Solve problems in contexts of pounds and pence	Reason
2	Targets: number sentences	14	Using and applying mathematics	Present solutions to puzzles and problems in an organised way	Reason
3	Find the cat: follow instructions	15	Using and applying mathematics	Explain decisions, methods and results in pictorial, spoken or written form, using mathematical language	Reason
4	Dominoes: numbers to 20	16	Counting and understanding number	Read and write numbers in figures and words	Refresh
5	Counting on and back (ITP)	17	Counting and understanding number	Count up to 100 objects by grouping them and counting in tens, fives or twos; explain what each digit in a two-digit number represents	Refine
6	Place value (ITP)	18	Counting and understanding number	Explain what each number in a two-digit number represents; partition two-digit numbers in different ways	Read
7	Twenty cards (ITP): order numbers	19	Counting and understanding number	Order two-digit numbers	Refine
8	Bricks: order numbers to 100	20	Counting and understanding number	Order two-digit numbers and position them on a number line	Reason

Highlighted text indicates the end-of-year objectives

Activity pages

Each page of teachers' notes includes:

Learning objectives
Covering the strands and objectives of the renewed *Primary Framework for Mathematics*

Type of starter
Identifying one or more of the 'six Rs' of oral and mental work (see page 7)

Whiteboard tools
Identifying the key functions of the accompanying CD-ROM activity

What to do
Outline notes on how to administer the activity with the whole class

Differentiation
Adapting the activity for more or less confident learners

Key questions
Probing questions to stimulate and sustain the oral and mental work

Annotations
At-a-glance instructions for using the CD-ROM activity.

Whiteboard hints and tips

Each title offers some general support identifying practical mathematical activities that can be performed on any interactive whiteboard (see pages 8–9).

Recording sheets

Two recording sheets have been included to support your planning:
- Planning for the six Rs: plan a balance of activities across the six Rs of mental and oral maths (see page 7).
- Star Maths Starters diary: build a record of the starters used (titles, objectives covered, how they were used and dates they were used).

WELL DONE!

About the CD-ROM

Types of activity

Each CD-ROM contains 30 interactive starter activities for use on any interactive whiteboard. These include:

Interactive whiteboard resources
A set of engaging interactive activities specifically designed for *Star Maths Starters*. The teachers' notes on pages 13–42 of this book explain how each activity can be used for a ten-minute mental maths starter, with annotated screen shots giving you at-a-glance support. Similarly, a 'what to do' function within each activity provides at-the-board support.

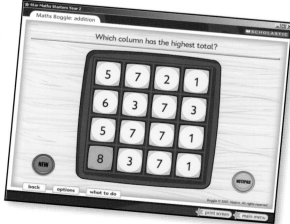

Interactive teaching programs (ITPs)

A small number of ITPs, originally developed by the National Numeracy Strategy, has been included on each CD-ROM. They are simple programs that model a range of objectives, such as data presentation or fraction bars. Their strength is that they are easy to read and use. If you press the Esc button the ITP will reduce to a window on the computer screen. It can then be enlarged or more ITPs can be launched and set up to model further objectives, or simply to extend the objective from that starter. To view the relevant 'what to do' notes once an ITP is open, press the Esc button to gain access to the function on the opening screen of the activity.

Interactive 'notepad'

A pop-up 'notepad' is built into a variety of activities. This allows the user to write answers or keep a record of workings out and includes 'pen', 'eraser' and 'clear' tools.

Teacher zone

This teachers' section includes links from the interactive activities to the *Primary Framework for Mathematics* strands, together with editable objectives grids, planning grids and printable versions of the activity sheets on pages 43–46.

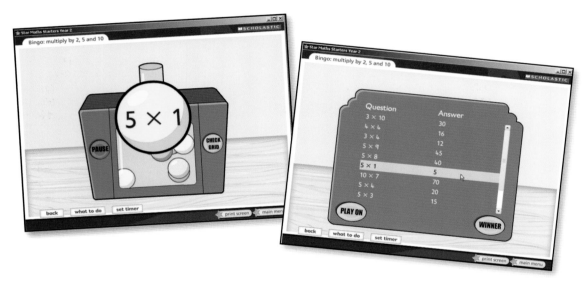

How to use the CD-ROM

System requirements

Minimum specification
- PC with a CD-ROM drive and 512 Mb RAM (recommended)
- Windows 98SE or above/Mac OSX.1 or above
- Recommended minimum processor speed: 1 GHz

Getting started

The *Star Maths Starters* CD-ROM should auto run when inserted into your CD drive. If it does not, use **My Computer** to browse the contents of the CD-ROM and click on the 'Star Maths Starters' icon.

From the start-up screen you will find four options: select **Credits** to view a list of credits. Click on **Register** to register the product to receive product updates and special offers. Click on **How to use** to access support notes for using the CD-ROM. Finally, if you agree to the terms and conditions, select **Start** to move to the main menu.

For all technical support queries, please phone Scholastic Customer Services on 0845 6039091.

The six Rs of oral and mental work

In the guidance paper *Renewing the Primary Framework for mathematics* (2006), the Primary National Strategy identified six features of children's mathematical learning that oral and mental work can support. The description of the learning and an outline of possible activities are given below:

Six Rs	Learning focus	Possible activities
Rehearse	To practise and consolidate existing skills, usually mental calculation skills, set in a context to involve children in problem solving through the use and application of these skills; use of vocabulary and language of number, properties of shapes or describing and reasoning.	Interpret words such as more, less, sum, altogether, difference, subtract; find missing numbers or missing angles on a straight line; say the number of days in four weeks or the number of 5p coins that make up 35p; describe part-revealed shapes, hidden solids; describe patterns or relationships; explain decisions or why something meets criteria.
Recall	To secure knowledge of facts, usually number facts; build up speed and accuracy; recall quickly names and properties of shapes, units of measure or types of charts, graphs to represent data.	Count on and back in steps of constant size; recite the 6-times table and derive associated division facts; name a shape with five sides or a solid with five flat faces; list properties of cuboids; state units of time and their relationships.
Refresh	To draw on and revisit previous learning; to assess, review and strengthen children's previously acquired knowledge and skills relevant to later learning; return to aspects of mathematics with which the children have had difficulty; draw out key points from learning.	Refresh multiplication facts or properties of shapes and associated vocabulary; find factor pairs for given multiples; return to earlier work on identifying fractional parts of given shapes; locate shapes in a grid as preparation for lesson on coordinates; refer to general cases and identify new cases.
Refine	To sharpen methods and procedures; explain strategies and solutions; extend ideas and develop and deepen the children's knowledge; reinforce their understanding of key concepts; build on earlier learning so that strategies and techniques become more efficient and precise.	Find differences between two two-digit numbers, extend to three-digit numbers to develop skill; find 10% of quantities, then 5% and 20% by halving and doubling; use audible and quiet counting techniques to extend skills; give coordinates of shapes in different orientations to hone concept; review informal calculation strategies.
Read	To use mathematical vocabulary and interpret images, diagrams and symbols correctly; read number sentences and provide equivalents; describe and explain diagrams and features involving scales, tables or graphs; identify shapes from a list of their properties; read and interpret word problems and puzzles; create their own problems and lines of enquiry.	Tell a story using an interactive bar chart; alter the chart for children to retell the story; starting with a number sentence (eg 2 + 11 = 13), children generate and read equivalent statements for 13; read values on scales with different intervals; read information about a shape and eliminate possible shapes; set number sentences in given contexts; read others' results and offer new questions and ideas for enquiry.
Reason	To use and apply acquired knowledge, skills and understanding; make informed choices and decisions, predict and hypothesise; use deductive reasoning to eliminate or conclude; provide examples that satisfy a condition always, sometimes or never and say why.	Sort shapes into groups and give reasons for selection; discuss why alternative methods of calculation work and when to use them; decide what calculation to do in a problem and explain the choice; deduce a solid from a 2D picture; use fractions to express proportions; draw conclusions from given statements to solve puzzles.

Each one of the styles of starter enables children to access different mathematical skills and each has a different outcome, as identified above. A bingo game, for example, provides a good way of rehearsing number facts, whereas a 'scales' activity supports reading skills. In the objectives grid on pages 10–11, the type of each Star Starters activity is identified to make it easier to choose appropriate styles of starter matched to a particular objective. A 'Six Rs' recording sheet has also been provided on page 12 (with an editable version on the CD-ROM) to track the types of starter you will be using against the strands of the renewed Framework.

Using the interactive whiteboard in primary mathematics

The interactive whiteboard is an invaluable tool for teaching and learning mathematics. It can be used to demonstrate and model mathematical concepts to the whole class, offering the potential to share children's learning experiences. It gives access to powerful resources – audio, video, images, websites and interactive activities – to discuss, interact with and learn from. *Star Maths Starters* provides 30 quality interactive resources that are easy to set up and use and which help children to improve their mathematical development and thinking skills through their use as short, focused oral and mental starters.

Whiteboard resources and children's learning

There are many reasons why the whiteboard, especially in mathematics, enhances children's learning:

- Using high-quality interactive maths resources will engage children in the process of learning and developing their mathematical thinking skills. Resources such as maths games can create a real sense of theatre in the whole class and promote a real desire to achieve and succeed in a task.
- As mentioned above, the whiteboard can be used to demonstrate some very important mathematical concepts. For example, many teachers find that children understand place value much faster and more thoroughly through using interactive resources on a whiteboard. Similarly, the whiteboard can support children's visualisation of mathematics, especially for 'Shape and Space' activities.
- Although mathematics usually has a correct or incorrect answer, there are often several ways of reaching the same result. The whiteboard allows the teacher to demonstrate methods and encourages children to present and compare their own mental or written methods of calculation.

Using a whiteboard in Year 2

An interactive whiteboard can be used for a variety of purposes in Year 2 mathematics lessons. These include:

- estimating and counting prepared sets of clipart objects – counting from a distance adds an extra degree of challenge to the children, so use the whiteboard tools to highlight sets or patterns to support them as appropriate;
- using interactive 100-square activities to practise times tables, highlight multiples and show number patterns (for example, showing the result of doubling and halving numbers);
- preparing shapes or sets of objects for children to find and demonstrate one half, one quarter and three quarters;
- using squared paper on the whiteboard to prepare a range of 2D shapes, pictures and patterns for the children to describe;
- using software programs to collect and organise data and show the results of class surveys in pictograms or bar charts.

Practical considerations

For the teacher, the whiteboard has the potential to save preparation and classroom time, as well as providing more flexible teaching.

ICT resources for the interactive whiteboard often involve numbers that are randomly generated, so that possible questions or calculations stemming from a single resource may be many and varied. This enables resources to be used for a longer or shorter time period depending on the purpose of the activity and how children's learning is progressing. *Star Maths Starters* includes many activities of this type.

From the very practical point of view of saving teachers' time, particularly in the starter activity, it is often easier to set up mathematics resources more quickly than those for other subjects. Once the software is familiar, preparation time is saved especially when there is need for clear presentation, as in drawing shapes accurately or creating charts and diagrams for 'Handling data' activities.

Maths resources on the interactive whiteboard are often flexible and enable differentiation so that a teacher can access different degrees of difficulty using the same software. Last but not least, whiteboard resources save time writing on the board and software often checks calculations, if required, which enables more time both for teaching and assessing children's understanding.

Using *Star Maths Starters* interactively

Much has been said and written about interactivity in the classroom but it is not always clear what this means. For example, children coming out to the board and ticking a box is not what is meant by 'whole-class interactive teaching and learning'. In mathematics it is about challenging children's ideas so that they develop their own thinking skills and, when appropriate, encouraging them to make connections across different mathematical topics. As a teacher, this means asking suitable questions and encouraging children to explore and discuss their methods of calculation and whether there are alternative ways of achieving the same result. *Star Maths Starters* provides some examples of key questions that could be asked while the activities are being undertaken, together with suggestions for how to engage less confident learners and stretch the more confident.

If you already have some experience in using the whiteboard interactively then we hope the teaching suggestions set out in this book will take you further. What is especially important is the facility the whiteboard provides to share pupils' mathematical learning experiences. This does not mean just asking children to suggest answers, but using the facility of the board to display and discuss ideas so that everyone can share in the learning experience. Obviously, this needs to be in a way that explores and relates the thinking of individuals to the context of the learning that is happening.

In the best whiteboard classrooms, teachers comment that the board provides a shared learning experience between the teacher and the class, in so far as the teacher may sometimes stand aside while children themselves are discussing their own mathematical methods and ideas.

Starter Number	Star Starter Title	Page No.	Strand	Learning objective as taken from the Primary Framework for Mathematics	Type of Starter
1	Shopping: money problems	13	Using and applying mathematics	Solve problems in contexts of pounds and pence	Reason
2	Targets: number sentences	14	Using and applying mathematics	Present solutions to puzzles and problems in an organised way	Reason
3	Find the cat: follow instructions	15	Using and applying mathematics	Explain decisions, methods and results in pictorial, spoken or written form, using mathematical language	Reason
4	Dominoes: numbers to 20	16	Counting and understanding number	Read and write numbers in figures and words	Refresh
5	Counting on and back (ITP)	17	Counting and understanding number	Count up to 100 objects by grouping them and counting in tens, fives or twos; explain what each digit in a two-digit number represents	Refine
6	Place value (ITP)	18	Counting and understanding number	Explain what each number in a two-digit number represents; partition two-digit numbers in different ways	Read
7	Twenty cards (ITP): order numbers	19	Counting and understanding number	Order two-digit numbers	Refine
8	Bricks: order numbers to 100	20	Counting and understanding number	Order two-digit numbers and position them on a number line	Reason
9	Fractions of shapes	21	Counting and understanding number	Find one half, one quarter and three quarters of shapes	Refine
10	Number spinners (ITP): addition and subtraction	22	Knowing and using number facts	Derive and recall all addition and subtraction facts for each number to at least 10	Refine
11	Bingo: addition and subtraction	23	Knowing and using number facts	Derive and recall all addition and subtraction facts for each number to at least 10	Recall
12	Halving and doubling to 20	24	Knowing and using number facts	Understand that halving is the inverse of doubling and derive and recall all doubles of numbers to 20 and the corresponding halves	Recall
13	Bingo: multiply by 2, 5 and 10	25	Knowing and using number facts	Derive and recall multiplication facts for the 2-, 5- and 10-times tables	Recall
14	Multiplication square: 2-, 5- and 10-times tables	26	Knowing and using number facts	Derive and recall the multiplication facts for the 2-, 5- and 10-times tables and the related division facts	Recall
15	Function machine: multiply by 2, 5 or 10	27	Knowing and using number facts	Recognise multiples of 2, 5 and 10	Reason

Starter Number	Star Starter Title	Page No.	Strand	Learning objective as taken from the Primary Framework for Mathematics	Type of Starter
16	Maths Boggle: addition	28	Calculating	Add mentally one-digit numbers	Rehearse
17	Beanstalk: addition and subtraction	29	Calculating	Add or subtract mentally a one-digit number to or from any two-digit number	Refine
18	Maths Boggle: addition and subtraction	30	Calculating	Add or subtract mentally a one-digit number to or from any two-digit number	Rehearse
19	Function machine: addition and subtraction	31	Calculating	Add or subtract mentally a one-digit number to or from any two-digit number	Reason
20	Number line (ITP): addition and subtraction	32	Calculating	Understand that subtraction is the inverse of addition and vice versa	Refine
21	Find the missing number: addition and subtraction	33	Calculating	Use the symbols + , – and = to record and interpret number sentences; calculate the value of an unknown in a number sentence	Refine
22	Find the missing number: multiplication and division	34	Calculating	Use the symbols ×, ÷ and = to record and interpret number sentences; calculate the value of an unknown in a number sentence	Reason
23	Dominoes: names of shapes	35	Understanding shape	Identify shapes from pictures of them	Recall
24	Reflection patterns	36	Understanding shape	Identify reflective symmetry in patterns	Refine
25	Maps and directions	37	Understanding shape	Follow and give instructions involving position, direction and movement	Read
26	Weighing scales: standard units	38	Measuring	Use standard units of weight	Rehearse
27	Measuring jug: read a scale	39	Measuring	Read the numbered divisions on a scale and interpret the divisions between them	Read
28	Fixing points (ITP): using a ruler	40	Measuring	Use a ruler to draw and measure lines to the nearest centimetre	Refine
29	Clocks: read the time	41	Measuring	Read the time to the quarter hour	Read
30	Block graph: favourite fruit	42	Handling data	Represent data using block graphs to show results	Refresh

Planning for the six Rs of oral and mental work

Oral and mental activity - six Rs	Using and applying mathematics	Counting and understanding number	Knowing and using number facts	Calculating	Understanding shape	Measuring	Handling data
Rehearse				• Maths Boggle: addition • Maths Boggle: addition and subtraction		• Weighing scales: standard units	
Recall			• Bingo: addition and subtraction • Halving and doubling to 20 • Bingo: multiply by 2, 5 and 10 • Multiplication square: 2-, 5- and 10-times tables		• Dominoes: names of shapes		
Refresh		• Dominoes: numbers to 20					• Block graph: favourite fruit
Refine		• Counting on and back (ITP) • Twenty cards (ITP); order numbers • Fractions of shapes	• Number spinners (ITP); addition and subtraction	• Beanstalk: addition and subtraction • Number line (ITP); addition and subtraction • Find the missing number: addition and subtraction	• Reflection patterns	• Fixing points (ITP); using a ruler	
Read		• Place value (ITP)			• Maps and directions	• Measuring jug: read a scale • Clocks: read the time	
Reason	• Shopping: money problems • Targets: number sentences • Find the cat: follow instructions	• Bricks: order numbers to 100	• Function machine: multiply by 2, 5 or 10	• Function machine: addition and subtraction • Find the missing number: multiplication and division			

Shopping: money problems

Strand

Using and applying mathematics

Learning objective

Solve problems in contexts of pounds and pence

Type of starter

Reason

Whiteboard tools
- Drag one item from the shelf into the basket.
- Press 'check-out' to move to next screen.
- Drag the exact amount (in coins) to the till to pay for each item.
- Press 'sale' to check if the amount paid is correct.
- Press 'back to shop' to start a new sale.

What to do

This activity introduces the children to coins of different values up to £2.00 and challenges them to work out the coins required to pay for individual items in a shop. Ask the children first to select an item and then drag it into the shopping basket. Next, challenge them to work out the exact coins required to pay for the item. Ask one child to come to the board to move the coins to the till. When each coin reaches the till, it remains visible, with the amount clearly shown. Press 'sale' to check whether the amount paid is correct. Record which coins the child used on the board and then ask for a different combination of coins to pay for the same item.

Differentiation

Less confident: select items that require fewer coins to build confidence (for example, the sticker album); allow more time for the children to work out the coins needed and if necessary supply them with toy (or real) money for additional support.
More confident: ask the children to find all the different combinations of coins to pay for an item.

Key questions
- *What coins could you use to pay for the item?*
- *What other coins could you use to pay for the item?*
- *The pens are priced £1.10. How many pence is this?*

'clear'
Press to clear till screen

shopping items
Drag one item for purchase to basket

'sale'
Press to check answer

'check-out'
Press to go to next screen

money
Drag correct amount of money to till

'back to shop'
Press to start a new sale

Targets: number sentences

Strand

Using and applying mathematics

Learning objective

Present solutions to puzzles and problems in an organised way

Type of starter

Reason

Whiteboard tools

- Press 'go' to generate five number cards.
- Press the blue circle to reveal the target number.
- Use the 'pen' tool in the 'notepad' to show calculations or to set an alternative target number. Press 'start again' or use the 'eraser' tool to delete any text.
- Press 'winner' if children complete the activity successfully to see the winner animation.

What to do

The aim of this activity is for the children to find the hidden target number in the 'bull's eye' by adding the numbers given on all five number cards shown. For example, if the target number is 24, the numbers produced may be 3, 9, 4, 6 and 2.
Suggest to the children that they use addition to make the target number. Try to identify the process that the children follow to find the target numbers. For example, do they put the numbers in size order to add them? Invite individuals to come to the board to write their calculations on the on-screen notepad (using the pencil tool), or write up the calculation for them. Encourage the rest of the class to suggest alternative methods to make, or get close to, the target answer.

Differentiation

Less confident: provide the children with number blocks as visual cues, or help them in organising the calculations. For additional support, provide each child with a copy of the photocopiable 'Targets' sheet on page 43.
More confident: set alternative target numbers using the onscreen 'notepad'and where possible, encourage the children to use simple subtraction and multiplication.

Key questions

- *What strategies are the most efficient? How do these strategies help you to 'hit the target'?*
- *What tips would you give somebody who was new to the game?*

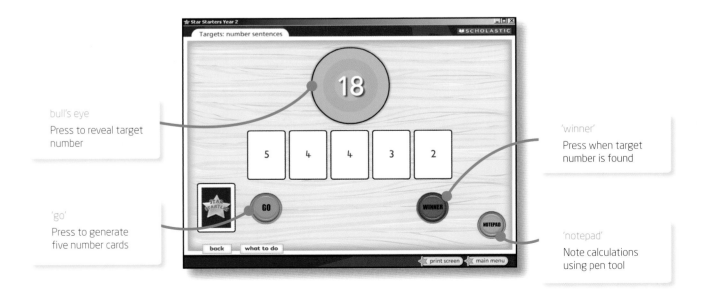

bull's eye
Press to reveal target number

'go'
Press to generate five number cards

'winner'
Press when target number is found

'notepad'
Note calculations using pen tool

Find the cat: follow instructions

Strand

Using and applying mathematics

Learning objective

Explain decisions, methods and results in pictorial, spoken or written form, using mathematical language

Type of starter

Reason

Whiteboard tools

● Type in the 'number across' and then the 'number up and down' to select a square.
● A keypad pops up automatically when you press on the white boxes to enter a number.
● Press 'check' to confirm the selection.
● Press 'new' to start a new game with the cat in a different position on the grid.

What to do

The aim of the activity is to find a cat in a square on a 4 × 4 grid, using reasoning skills and appropriate mathematical vocabulary. The position of the cat is randomly selected for each game. Explain to the children how they should select 'number up' and 'number across' to identify each square and how they might use these numbers to describe the position of different squares. After each selection, the square will be revealed. If the cat has not been revealed, ask the children about the remaining possible squares in which the cat might be hiding. At all stages ask them to describe the square they are selecting as well as giving its number. For example: *The square above the watering can. The top middle square,* and so on. To narrow the selections and to prevent the activity becoming a guessing game, one of three messages appears after each selection: 'number across correct' and 'number up correct' indicate that either the column or row is correct; 'have another go!' indicates that neither column nor row is correct. When the cat has been found, the garden is completed and a *miaow* sound is heard! Children should respond positively to this activity and learn to develop a strategy for finding the cat in the fewest possible attempts, using the hints where necessary.

Differentiation

Less confident: check carefully that the children understand how to identify each square.
More confident: ask children to describe their strategies for identifying the correct square.

Key questions

● *How can we describe, for example, the square in the top-left corner?*
● *Which square is above the mole? To the right of the flower?*
● *Which squares have not yet been picked? Which squares have been picked?*

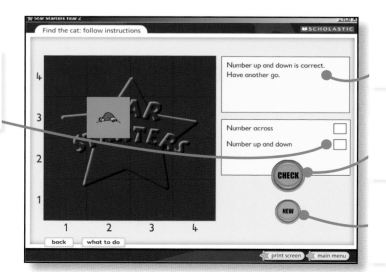

'number across' and 'number up and down'
Enter to select square where cat may be hiding

hints
Use this message to help you decide which square to try next

'check'
Press to confirm choice

'new'
Press to start new game

Dominoes: numbers to 20

Strand

Counting and understanding number

Learning objective

Read and write numbers in figures and words

Type of starter

Refresh

Whiteboard tools

● Press 'new' to start a new game.
● Press 'miss a go' to take another domino from the pot.
● Drag and drop the dominoes into the playing space. Rotate each domino through 90° by pressing the top right-hand corner.
● Press 'winner' if Player 1 or Player 2 has placed all of the dominoes and it is agreed that the last domino was placed correctly.

What to do

The aim of this activity is to match numbers written as words with the equivalent digits up to 20: for example, 'nineteen' matches with '19'. The activity is played in the same way as standard dominoes, with two 'players' or teams playing against each other. Each player (or team) is dealt four dominoes, with the others left in a central pot. A starter domino is selected by the computer to begin the game, and the players then take turns to play. If a player is unable to place a domino, they should press 'miss a go' and take one from the central pot. The game continues until one player places all of their dominoes, and is declared the winner, or there are no more dominoes left in the pot. If a stalemate situation occurs - in which neither player is able to put down a domino and the pot is empty - the player with fewest remaining dominoes is declared the winner.

   It should be noted that there is no automatic checking of whether dominoes are in the correct position - this is left to the agreement of the players.

Differentiation

Less confident: let the children use talk partners to discuss moves, which will help to boost confidence and affirm their decisions.
More confident: play 'beat the teacher', in which children pit themselves against an adult in the classroom.

Key questions

● *Which strategies did you use to place dominoes? How could you block your opponent?*
● *Which digit matches this number? Which number name matches this digit?*

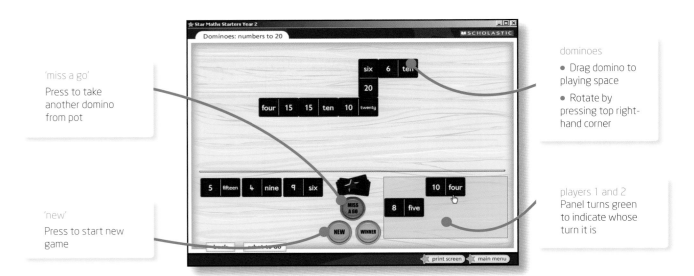

'miss a go'
Press to take another domino from pot

'new'
Press to start new game

dominoes
● Drag domino to playing space
● Rotate by pressing top right-hand corner

players 1 and 2
Panel turns green to indicate whose turn it is

Counting on and back (ITP)

Strand

Counting and understanding number

Learning objective

Count up to 100 objects by grouping them and counting in tens, fives or twos; explain what each digit in a two-digit number represents

Type of starter

Refine

Whiteboard tools
● Press the upper '00' button to show or hide the number of beads on the left of the string.
● Press the lower '00' button to show or hide the bead number.
● Press a bead to move one or several beads along the string.
● Press '-/+ 1' or '-/+ 10' to move groups of beads.

What to do
The aim of this activity is for the children to refine their understanding of place value to 100 using a 100-bead string as a support. The bead string will enable you to model a variety of different counting and calculation strategies.

The screen shows a horizontal string of beads. By pressing on selected beads, you can move individual beads or groups of beads to the right or left of the string. Pressing the circular beads at either end will move all the beads to the opposite end. By default, moving over a bead will show the bead number; however, this function can be turned off by pressing the lower of the two buttons marked '00'. Similarly, the numbers of beads on the left of the string are automatically shown on the display; this function can also be turned off by pressing the upper button marked '00'. Pressing the controls marked '-1', '-10', '+1' and '+10', allows you to move either 1 or 10 beads to the left or right of the string. Count in steps of 1, 2, 5 and 10 and ask the children to make predictions about the number of beads to the left or right of the string.

Differentiation
Less confident: encourage the children to count the beads using other class resources as support (for example, 100- or 10-bead strings if available). Help the children to make their own bead counters for counting activities at home or in school.
More confident: increase the increment steps. For example, you might ask the children: *Can you use the beads to predict what 20 more than 24 is?*

Key questions
● *Why do you think the beads on the whiteboard are in different colours? How can this help us to count?*
● *How many beads are there if I continue to count in twos... fives...?*

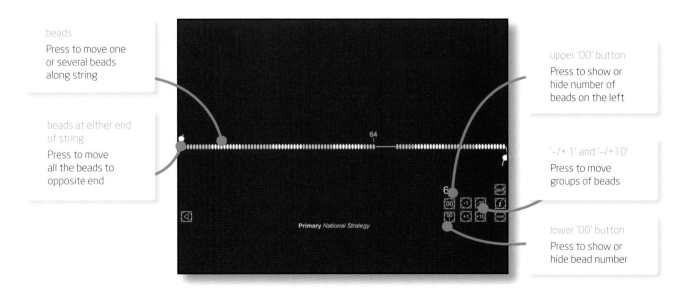

beads
Press to move one or several beads along string

beads at either end of string
Press to move all the beads to opposite end

upper '00' button
Press to show or hide number of beads on the left

'-/+ 1' and '-/+10'
Press to move groups of beads

lower '00' button
Press to show or hide bead number

Primary *National Strategy*

Place value (ITP)

Strand

Counting and understanding number

Learning objective

Explain what each number in a two-digit number represents; partition two-digit numbers in different ways

Type of starter

Read

Whiteboard tools

- Press the pointers to select the hundreds, tens and units digits, then press the number in the circles to display them as place value cards.
- Drag and drop each card to reposition them.
- Press the cross in the top left-hand corner of a card to delete it.
- Press the pointer below the number to show it as a group of counters.
- Press 'clear' to clear all place value cards from the screen.

What to do

This activity allows you to partition three-digit whole numbers, using place value cards. Create a card by pressing each of the three number boxes at the foot of the screen, which determine the value of each card. The left-hand box creates the hundreds, the centre box the tens and the right-hand box the units. Press the pointers above and below each button to select each number, and press the numbered circle to display it as a 'card'.

Use this activity to secure the children's understanding of place value. By displaying two sets of cards at the same time, you can compare their values and pose questions about their sum and difference. You can reposition a card by pressing it, and delete a card by pressing the cross in the top left-hand corner. Use these features to partition and re-arrange the numbers, helping the children to begin to understand how pencil-and-paper methods of calculation are recorded.

Differentiation

Less confident: press the pointer at the foot of each card to reveal the number as groups of counters; ask the children to use these counters to support their understanding of the size of each number.

More confident: ask the children to 'explode' (or partition) a three-digit number: for example, 152 would explode to make 100, 50 and 2. Encourage them to write each number on their individual whiteboards.

Key questions

- *How would you break down this number? Demonstrate with the counters.*
- *How would you read this number? What does each digit in the number represent?*

move card
Press and drag a card to reposition it

counters
Press pointer below number to show it as a group of counters

delete card
Press cross in top left-hand corner to delete card

three number boxes
Press arrows to select hundreds, tens and units digits

126

100 20 6 clear quit

Primary National Strategy

Twenty cards (ITP): order numbers

Strand

Counting and understanding number

Learning objective

Order two-digit numbers

Type of starter

Refine

Whiteboard tools
● Press the top left-hand button to set parameters. Select 'random cards' from the menu and then select the following options: 'How many cards' 5; 'Maximum number' 20; 'Minimum number' 10.
● Press the 'deal' and 'spread' buttons to deal the stack of cards and spread them around the screen.
● Press the red area of a card to turn it face-up.
● Move a card by pressing the central blue area and dragging it.

What to do
Use this ITP initially to rehearse the ordering of numbers to 20, but move up to higher two-digit numbers in subsequent sessions. The ITP generates individual cards (or stacks of cards) which appear face down. You can move them around the screen and turn them over to display the numbers. The top left-hand button (featuring cards with a blue outline) allows you to set parameters for the cards (see Whiteboard tools above). Use the ITP to display groups of different numbers that children can compare and order. Ask the whole class to suggest the order, or invite individuals to come to the board to order the numbers. The cards may be sequenced or produced as a random set, and dealt in numerical order or shuffled. This activity can support work on identifying, describing, extending and generating sequences.

Differentiation
Less confident: keep the maximum number at 20. Ask the children to order them on the board with support if necessary.
More confident: encourage the children to predict the next number in a sequence and to identify a pattern, extending the pattern beyond the number range on the screen.

Key questions
● *Can you predict the number pattern in this stack without looking at all the numbers?*
● *What strategies could we use to begin ordering the numbers?*

turn card
Press the red area to turn over a card

move card
Press the blue area to move a card

'random cards' menu
Use this dialogue box to set parameters

single cards
Press pointers, then the circle, to create single numbered cards

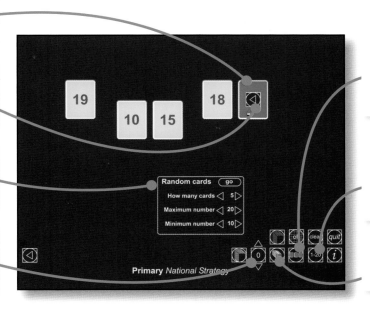

deal
Press to deal in a line

1–20
Press to create 20 cards numbered 1 to 20

'random' deal
Press to deal randomly

Bricks: order numbers to 100

Strand

Counting and understanding number

Learning objective

Order two-digit numbers and position them on a number line

Type of starter

Reason

Whiteboard tools
- Press 'go' to generate five bricks, each showing a number between 1 and 100.
- Drag each brick into the gaps in the wall, with the smallest number positioned in the lowest position on the wall.
- If five bricks are positioned correctly, a 'Well done' message appears. If any bricks are placed incorrectly, they snap back to their starting positions.
- Select 'options', then 'fix first digit' to keep the tens digit the same on all five bricks.

What to do

Use this activity either to rehearse the children's understanding of ordering numbers to 100, or to probe their reasoning. Press 'go' to reveal five bricks, each showing a number between 1 and 100. Ask the children to work as a whole class to decide the correct order, in pairs by writing down the correct sequence on their individual whiteboards, or individually. Position the bricks in the wall by dragging and dropping them, or ask individual children to place them for you. Probe for any misconceptions and ask for strategies that the children used to order the numbers.

Differentiation

Less confident: use a number line to support the children's ordering skills before positioning the bricks in the wall. Fix the first digit to keep the tens digit the same on each brick.
More confident: ask the children what would need to be added to the top brick to make 100. Ask for other numbers that fall between two selected bricks.

Key questions
- *Which are the smallest and largest numbers on these five bricks?*
- *What would the new number be if 10... 20... 30... were added to the number on the lowest brick?*

bricks
Order by dragging into wall

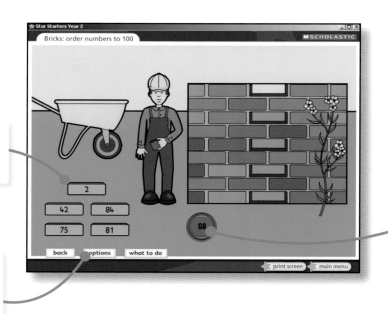

'go'
Press to generate new set of bricks

'options'
Fix first digit if required

Fractions of shapes

Strand

Counting and understanding number

Learning objective

Find one half, one quarter and three quarters of shapes

Type of starter

Refine

Whiteboard tools

● Press 'options' to change the grid size. Select 10 to make a 10 × 10 grid.
● Press on a square in the grid to change the colour. Press several squares to build up a shape.
● Select a colour from the colour palette to change the colour of the squares on the grid. If part of a shape needs to be removed, press the white square before pressing the coloured squares you wish to remove.
● Press 'clear' to remove all coloured squares from the screen.

What to do

Before the lesson starts, create several rectangles on the screen – made up of two, four, eight, twelve, sixteen or twenty squares which are all the same colour. Using the colour palette, re-colour one half, one quarter or three quarters of each shape. During the starter activity, ask the children to tell you what fraction of the rectangle is coloured differently. Then repeat the activity using a different rectangle, again with a fraction coloured in. Invite individuals to come to the board to demonstrate one half and one quarter of selected shapes using the method described above. Move on to three quarters in subsequent sessions.

This activity can also easily be extended to find thirds and sixths, or fifths and tenths, of rectangular shapes.

Differentiation

Less confident: limit the activity to halves and quarters of the selected shapes. Work with the children to demonstrate 'one half' and 'one quarter' using flat shapes.
More confident: ask the children if they can describe different ways of saying the same fraction, such as: *One half is the same as two quarters*.

Key questions

● *What fraction of the whole shape is blue?*
● *What would you have to add to the blue fraction to make a whole?*

palette
Press your chosen colour to build up a shape

'options'
Specify grid size

white square
If part of a shape needs to be removed, select the white square, then press on the coloured squares in the grid you wish to remove

Number spinners (ITP): addition and subtraction

Strand

Knowing and using number facts

Learning objective

Derive and recall all addition and subtraction facts for each number to at least 10

Type of starter

Refine

Whiteboard tools
● Use the arrows on the left-hand button to select the range of numbers covered by the spinners.
● Press the middle button to select either 3-, 4-, 5- or 6-sided number spinners.
● Press the arrows on the right-hand button to select the number of spinners displayed on the screen (1–3).
● Spinners: press the central yellow dot to spin the spinner; press any number on the spinner to increase it by 1.

What to do
The aim of this ITP is to generate random numbers using 'spinners' with 3, 4, 5 or 6 sides. Using the pointers on the right-hand button, you can create one, two or three spinners at a time. The pointers on the middle button allow you to select the number of sides. Once this has been determined, press the shape inside the button to display the spinners. By pressing the central yellow circle on the spinner, you can spin the spinner to generate a random number (as identified by the red arrow beneath each spinner).

Use this ITP to create incomplete number sentences to refine understanding of number bonds to 10 and above (for example, 2 + 7+ ? = 10 or 10 – 9 = ?). Also, use one spinner to generate a single digit and ask the children to write another number on their individual whiteboards to make a target total, such as 10 or 15.

Differentiation
Less confident: use three spinners to add three random numbers together. In this case, reduce the number range to 1–4 and use a four-sided spinner.
More confident: select a higher number range (numbers up to 20 or 30, for example) and two spinners.

Key questions
● *What is the missing number?*
● *How could this be written as an addition or subtraction number sentence?*

spinners
● Press the yellow dot to spin
● Press an individual number to increase it by 1

number range
Press the arrows to select range of numbers

number of spinners
Press the arrows to select number of spinners

shape button
Press to select type of spinner

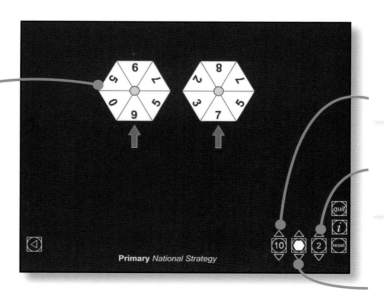

Primary National Strategy

Bingo: addition and subtraction

Strand

Knowing and using number facts

Learning objective

Derive and recall all addition and subtraction facts for each number to at least 10

Type of starter

Recall

Whiteboard tools
● Print bingo cards from the opening screen.
● Press 'set timer' to adjust the time between bingo calls (5–20 seconds).
● Press 'start' to begin a new game.
● Press 'check grid' to check the answers if someone calls *House*.
● Press 'play on' or 'winner' after checking a player's grid.

What to do

The aim of this activity is to improve the children's recall of adddition and subtraction facts to 10 and above. Ask the children to play individually or organise them into pairs; provide each child or pair with a bingo card (these can be printed from the opening screen or prepared using the bingo card template on page 44).

Each ball offers an addition or subtraction sentence. Explain to the children that If the answer appears on their bingo grid, they should mark it off. If the children are new to the game, allow for a longer amount of time between bingo calls. If a child calls *House* (or other similar winning call), press the 'check grid' button to pause the game and call up the checking grid, which includes all of the number sentences that have been called. If they are correct, press the 'winner' button to hear an appropriate fanfare. If they are not correct, press 'play on' to continue the game.

Differentiation

Less confident: allow children to to use tens blocks to support this activity. Also, allow a longer time period between each bingo call.
More confident: increase the number of answers on the bingo cards, using the blank bingo cards on photocopiable page 44.

Key questions
● *How do you know that all of your answers are correct?*
● *What strategies did you use to remember these number facts?*

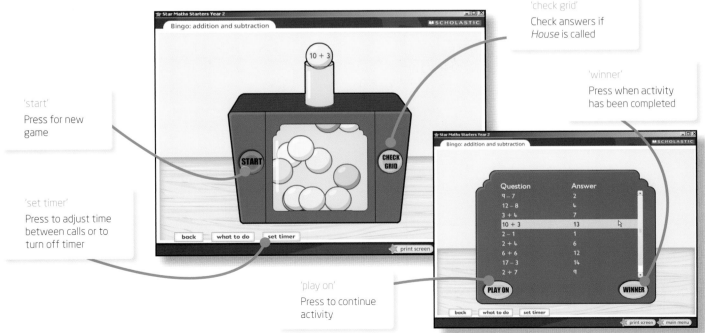

'check grid'
Check answers if *House* is called

'winner'
Press when activity has been completed

'start'
Press for new game

'set timer'
Press to adjust time between calls or to turn off timer

'play on'
Press to continue activity

Question	Answer
9 – 7	2
12 – 8	4
3 + 4	7
10 + 3	13
2 – 1	1
2 + 4	6
6 + 6	12
17 – 3	14
2 + 7	9

Halving and doubling to 20

Strand

Knowing and using number facts

Learning objective

Understand that halving is the inverse of doubling and derive and recall all doubles of numbers to 20 and the corresponding halves

Type of starter

Recall

Whiteboard tools
● From the 'options' menu, select: squares on a side: 10; start number: 1; step: 1.
● Press 'hide' to conceal all the columns from 3 onwards.
● Press the 'highlight' button to highlight a double and its half.
● Press 'clear' to reveal all hidden numbers.

What to do
Before the lesson, prepare the multiplication square as directed above. At the start of the activity, ask the children to say aloud *double 1 is 2, double 2 is 4,* and so on, up to double 10. Next, hide all the doubles and challenge the children to give you all of them in random order by highlighting different numbers in the 'ones' column. After each selection, press the square – using 'clear' to confirm or refute their answers. Then reverse the process by starting with any 'double number' and asking for its half.

Differentiation
Less confident: suggest that the children look at the numbers surrounding the double that is hidden. Provide them with number grids to help them find the answer.
More confident: ask the children for doubles beyond 10, such as *double 15, halve 40.*

Key questions
● *What is the double of ___?* (Select the number of your choice.)
● *What is half ___?* (Again, select the number of your choice.)

'highlight'
Press to highlight numbers

'hide'
Press to hide numbers

'clear'
Press to reveal hidden numbers

'options'
Press to set parameters for activity

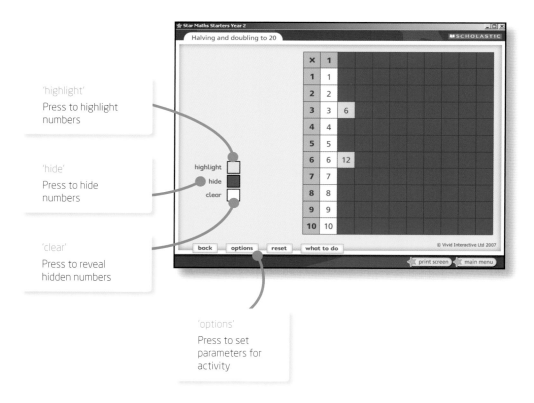

Bingo: multiply by 2, 5 and 10

Strand

Knowing and using number facts

Learning objective

Derive and recall multiplication facts for the 2-, 5- and 10-times tables

Type of starter

Recall

Whiteboard tools

- Print bingo cards from the opening screen.
- Press 'set timer' to adjust the time between bingo calls (5–20 seconds).
- Press 'start' to begin a new game.
- Press 'check grid' to check the answers if someone calls *House*.
- Press 'play on' or 'winner' after checking a player's grid.

What to do

The aim of this activity is to improve the children's quick recall of their 2-, 5- or 10-times tables. Ask the children to play individually or organise them into pairs; provide each child or pair with a bingo card (these can be printed from the opening screen or prepared using the bingo card template on page 44).

Once the activity has begun, the children have to match the multiplication questions, displayed or called out, to the answers given on their grids. Explain to them that If the answer appears on their bingo grid, they should mark it off. If the children are new to the game, allow for a longer amount of time between bingo calls. If a child calls *House* (or other similar winning call), press the 'check grid' button to pause the game and call up the checking grid, which includes all of the number sentences that have been called. If they are correct, press the 'winner' button to hear an appropriate fanfare. If they are not correct, press 'play on' to continue the game.

Differentiation

Less confident: support the children with a 2-, 5- and 10-times table grid.
More confident: increase the number of answers on the bingo cards, using the blank grids on photocopiable page 44.

Key questions

- *How do you know that all of your answers are correct?*
- *What strategies did you use to work out these multiples quickly?*

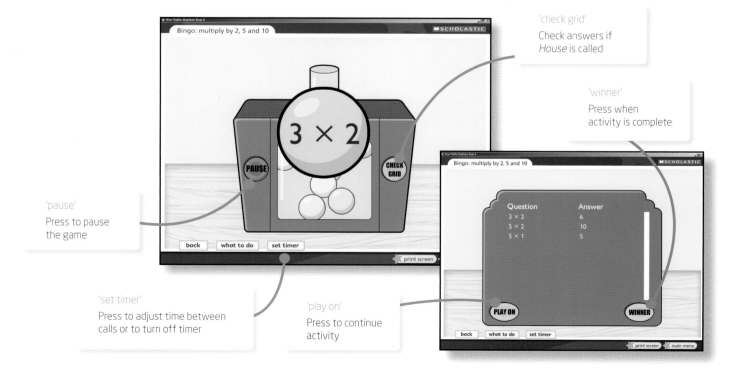

'check grid'
Check answers if *House* is called

'winner'
Press when activity is complete

'pause'
Press to pause the game

'set timer'
Press to adjust time between calls or to turn off timer

'play on'
Press to continue activity

Multiplication square: 2-, 5- and 10-times tables

Strand

Knowing and using number facts

Learning objective

Derive and recall the multiplication facts for the 2-, 5- and 10-times tables and the related division facts

Type of starter

Recall

Whiteboard tools
- From the 'options' menu, select: squares on a side: 10; start number: 1; step: 1.
- Press 'hide' to conceal all columns except columns 1, 2, 5 and 10.
- Press 'highlight' to highlight a number.
- Press 'clear' to reveal hidden numbers.

What to do
Before the lesson, prepare the multiplication square as directed above. At the start of the activity, ask the children to count on and back in twos using the second column. Next, ask them to count on and back in fives while pointing to the fives column. To recall the multiplication facts for 2, highlight one of the squares in the second column, then ask the children what number multiplied by 2 would give this number. For example, you might highlight the number 10 in column 2, and ask: *What number multiplied by 2 gives 10?* Then ask the children for the related division fact: *What is 10 divided by 2?* If the children are confident, continue this procedure using columns 5 and 10.

Differentiation
Less confident: involve the children who are less confident in finding multiples of lower numbers in the column.
More confident: ask the children to tell you the number sentence associated with each multiple.

Key questions
- *What number multiplied by 2 gives 10?*
- *What is 10 divided by 2?*

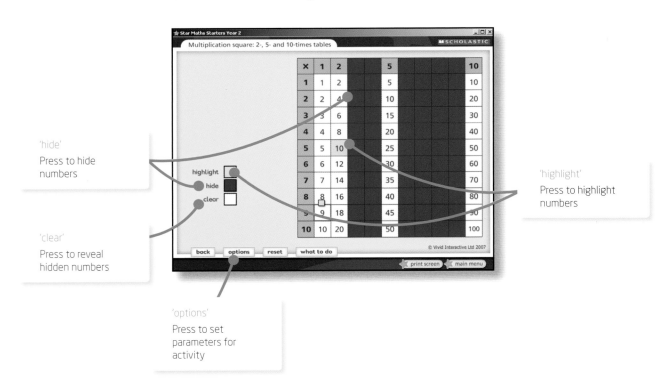

'hide'
Press to hide numbers

'clear'
Press to reveal hidden numbers

'highlight'
Press to highlight numbers

'options'
Press to set parameters for activity

Function machine: multiply by 2, 5 or 10

Strand

Knowing and using number facts

Learning objective

Recognise multiples of 2, 5 and 10

Type of starter

Reason

Whiteboard tools

- Use the 'options' menu to set the 'machine mode'. Select from 'manual' or 'random' options.
- Select 'manual' to enable you to prepare your own number sentences, or 'random' to produce a computer-generated number sentence.
- A keypad pops up automatically when you press a window to enable you to enter a number.
- Press the 'history' button to view a list of the number sentences completed during the lesson.

What to do

The aim of this game is to find the missing number or function to complete a number sentence. Either the teacher or the computer can generate these numbers using either the 'manual' or 'random' mode options.

Random mode: the computer selects a number sentence, but hides the input, output and function windows on the machine. Decide which element to reveal first and press that window to open it. After one other element has been revealed, ask the children to write down and then display the missing number or function. Check their answers and then press 'go' to check the answer on the machine. The computer will generate both multiplication and division sentences in the 2-, 5- and 10-times tables.

Manual mode: enter some number sentences involving multiplication or division in the 2-, 5- or 10-times tables. Again, press 'go' to check answers.

Differentiation

Less confident: in 'manual' mode create sentences using one times table (eg ×2) to develop children's confidence before introducing division facts and a wider range of times tables.

More confident: invite a volunteer to create a number sentence in 'manual' mode for the rest of the class to work out.

Key questions

- *How can you work out the missing parts of the number sentence?*
- *How much do I need to show you before you can complete this number sentence?*

'new'
- Press to start again in 'manual' mode
- Press for number sentence in 'random' mode

'options'
- Select 'manual' mode to enter your own numbers
- Select 'random' mode for computer-generated numbers, initially hidden

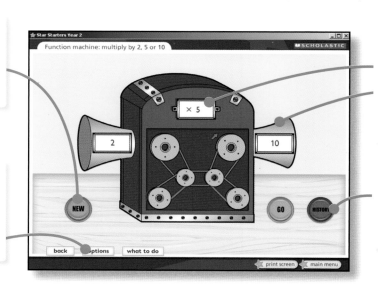

windows
- Type numbers and functions in 'manual' mode
- Press to open in 'random' mode

'history'
Use to track completed number sentences

Maths Boggle: addition

Strand

Calculating

Learning objective

Add mentally one-digit numbers

Type of starter

Rehearse

Whiteboard tools
● Press 'new' to rattle the dice and start a new game.
● Highlight each of the dice by pressing it once (to remove the highlight, press again).
● Select a target question from the 'options' menu at the foot of the screen.
● Use the 'notepad' to show calculations or to write a target number.

What to do

The aim of this activity is to use mental methods of addition to estimate and then work out which number string (column or row) gives the highest or lowest totals. In this version of the activity, the number strings include numbers between 1 and 10.

Start by selecting a question from the 'options' menu at the foot of the screen (or, should you wish, by setting your own question). Explain the terms 'columns' and 'rows' if necessary. The dice are 'rattled' to reveal a random selection of numbers. In pairs or individually, the children find the answer to each question by calculating using the numbers on the screen. Answers can be checked by highlighting individual rows or columns. Highlight the children's selections and show the calculation using the on-screen notepad.

Differentiation

Less confident: ask the children to find number pairs that make a target total (for example, 10).
More confident: ask the children to prepare some of their own questions for the rest of the class to answer.

Key questions
● *What strategies did you use to add the numbers?*
● *How can you quickly check your answers?*

dice
Press to highlight

'new'
Press to rattle dice

'options'
Select questions from menu

'notepad'
Note calculations on pad using the pen tool

Boggle © 2007, Hasbro. All rights reserved.

Beanstalk: addition and subtraction

Strand

Calculating

Learning objective

Add or subtract mentally a one-digit number to or from any two-digit number

Type of starter

Refine

Whiteboard tools
- Starting point: Jack always starts at 0.
- Move Jack up and down the beanstalk in steps of 1 to answer the maths problem or number sentence shown on screen.
- Select options to generate different types of maths problem – select from 'up only' (addition) or 'up and down' (addition and subtraction) options.
- Press 'notepad' and use the pen tool to show methods of working out the answers or to set a new question.
- Press 'answer' to reveal the completed number sentence.
- Press 'new' to move Jack back to the starting point and to generate a new problem.

What to do

Use this activity to practise the addition and subtraction of numbers to 24. The activity sets a range of number problems based on the 'Jack and the Beanstalk' theme. Encourage the children to use their individual whiteboards so that they can work out the answers for themselves prior to any class discussion. Extend the activity beyond the initial question by asking, for example: *What would happen if Jack now moves down eight steps?* Illustrate this by dragging and dropping Jack to the new position.

Differentiation

Less confident: use the 'up only' option at first until the children understand how Jack moves up the beanstalk. Use the photocopiable 'Beanstalk' sheet on page 45 to support the children's calculations.
More confident: using the 'up only' option, ask the children extra questions that would move Jack beyond the 24 mark (though this cannot be demonstrated on screen). Ask the children to use the photocopiable page for their answers.

Key questions
- *On which number does Jack end up? How did you work this out?*
- *How far up or down the beanstalk would Jack need to climb to reach the number ___?* (You can change the number as you wish.)

'new'

Press to move Jack back to starting point and to set a new problem

'options'
- Select 'up only' or 'up and down'
- Show or hide number sentence

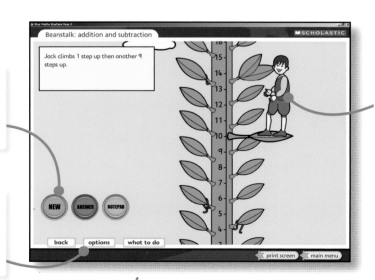

Jack

Drag Jack up or down the beanstalk

Maths Boggle: addition and subtraction

Strand

Calculating

Learning objective

Add or subtract mentally a one-digit number to or from any two-digit number

Type of starter

Rehearse

Whiteboard tools
- Press 'new' to rattle the dice and start a new game.
- Highlight each of the dice by pressing it once (to remove the highlight, press again).
- Select a target question from the 'options' menu at the foot of the screen.
- Use the 'notepad' to show calculations or set a new question.

What to do

The aim of this activity is to use mental methods to answer a range of questions involving the addition and subtraction of numbers to 20.

Start by selecting a question from the 'options' menu at the foot of the screen (or, should you wish, by setting your own question). Explain the terms 'columns' and 'rows' if necessary. The dice are 'rattled' to reveal a selection of numbers to 20. In pairs or individually, the children find the answer to each question by calculating using the numbers on the screen. Answers can be checked by highlighting individual rows or columns. Highlight the children's selections and show the calculation using the on-screen notepad. Focus on pairs of numbers in this activity using questions such as: *How many number sentences can you make from the numbers in this row/column? What is the difference between these two numbers?*

Differentiation

Less confident: ask the children to add or subtract pairs of numbers on the grid.
More confident: challenge children with questions such as: *Who can make the lowest total using all of the numbers in this row/column?*

Key questions
- *Who found the lowest/highest total? How do you know this is the lowest/highest total?*
- *How can you quickly check your answers?* (Answers might include: finding doubles or multiples of a number; adding near doubles; identifying number bonds.)

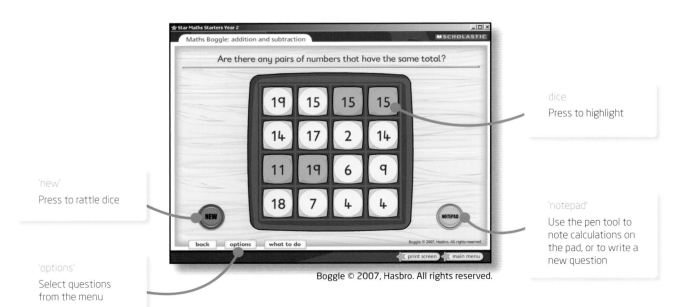

Boggle © 2007, Hasbro. All rights reserved.

Function machine: addition and subtraction

Strand

Calculating

Learning objective

Add or subtract mentally a one-digit number to or from any two-digit number

Type of starter

Reason

Whiteboard tools

- Use the 'options' menu to set the 'machine mode'. Select from 'manual' or 'random' options.
- Select 'manual' to enable you to prepare your own number sentences, or 'random' to produce a computer-generated number sentence.
- A keypad pops up when you press on a window to enable you to enter a number.
- Press the 'history' button to view a list of the number sentences completed during the lesson.

What to do

The aim of this game is to find the missing number or function to complete a number sentence. Either the teacher or the computer can generate these numbers using either the 'manual' or 'random' mode options.

Random mode: the computer selects a number sentence, but hides the input, output and function windows on the machine. Decide which element to reveal first and press that window to open it. After one other element has been revealed, ask the children to write down and then display the missing number or function. Check their answers and then press 'go' to check the answer on the machine. The computer will generate both addition and subtraction sentences.

Manual mode: enter some number sentences involving the addition or subtraction of a single-digit number with a two-digit number. For example: 19 + 2, 21 + 3, 32 + 7, 19 + 5. Ask the children to work out the answer, then press 'go' to reveal the completed sentence.

Differentiation

Less confident: in 'manual' mode, create some simple addition sentences involving number facts to 20 to develop children's confidence. Support the children with larger two-digit addition and subtraction sentences.

More confident: ask one of the children to create a number sentence in 'manual' mode for the rest of the class to work out.

Key questions

- *How can you work out the missing parts of the number sentence?*
- *How much do I need to show you before you can complete this number sentence?*

'new'
- Press to start again in 'manual' mode
- Press for number sentence in 'random' mode

'options'
- Select 'manual' mode to enter your own numbers
- Select 'random' mode for computer-generated numbers, initially hidden

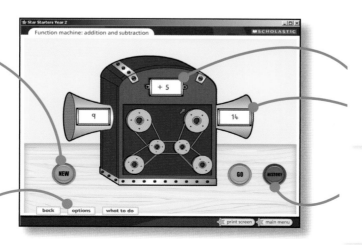

windows
- Type numbers and functions in 'manual' mode
- Press to open in 'random' mode

'history'
Use to track completed number sentences

Number line (ITP): addition and subtraction

Strand

Calculating

Learning objective

Understand that subtraction is the inverse of addition and vice versa

Type of starter

Refine

Whiteboard tools
- Press 'max' and 'min' to fix the range of numbers (between –30 and 500).
- Drag the circles to make markers on the line.
- Show or hide some or all of the number sentence.
- Show or hide the span (difference) box.

What to do

The aim of this activity is to refine the skills that the children need when adding or subtracting pairs of numbers, using a number line as a support. When this program is launched it shows a simple number line running from 0 to 20. For the purposes of this activity, press the right-hand 'max' pointer and increase the length of the number line to 100. Next, press and drag the circle below the left-hand end of the number line until it rests over 70; then drag the circle on the left until it rests over 30. Ask the children to predict the difference between the two numbers, 30 and 70. Continue the activity by moving the right-hand marker a few more times to create new subtraction sentences. The correct number sentence can be revealed by pressing '? + ? =', and the span (difference) between the two numbers can be shown using the upper and lower buttons appearing second from the right. Go through a few examples with the number in the spanning box shown and then challenge individual children to work out number sentences with the number in the spanning box (or the complete number sentence) hidden.

Differentiation

Less confident: lower the range using the 'max' button to build children's confidence.
More confident: use the top row of buttons to show or hide the different parts of the number sentence until only the answer can be seen. Ask the children: *What other pairs of numbers could be used to give the same answer?*

Key questions
- *Where should I look to find the difference number? What is this number?*
- *Are there different numbers that would make the same answer?*

70 – ? = 40

circles below number line
Drag circles to make markers on the line

'max' and 'min'
Use to fix the range of numbers (anywhere between –30 and 500)

top row of buttons
Press to show or hide some or all of number sentence

span button
Press to show or hide span (difference) box

Primary *National Strategy*

Find the missing number: addition and subtraction

Strand

Calculating

Learning objective

Use the symbols + , – and = to record and interpret number sentences; calculate the value of an unknown in a number sentence

Type of starter

Refine

Whiteboard tools

● Move cards and symbols onto the line to build a number sentence.
● Drag and drop numbers and symbols within a line to re-order them.
● Drag cards off the line to remove them.
● Press 'reset' to clear the cards and symbols from the screen and start again.

What to do

This activity encourages children to read number sentences as well as do the calculations. Create a number sentence and then ask the children to read it out. Numbers of any size can be selected, as two digits selected consecutively snap together to form a two-digit number. Ask the children for the answer to the calculation and then invite them to read the number sentence again, inserting the previously missing number. Initially, use numbers up to 20 and prepare number sentences with just one element missing, such as $\triangle + 5 = 11$. Then move on to examples in which two symbols are used to stand for unknown numbers (for example, $\square - \triangle = 30$).

Differentiation

Less confident: before starting the activity, check that the children understand that the symbols stand for unknown numbers. Go through a few examples with them.
More confident: ask the children to make up their own number sentences on the whiteboard and read these out. Challenge the whole class to calculate the answer.

Key questions

● *Can you read this number sentence?*
● *What number could this symbol stand for? What other numbers could it be?*

number sentence
Drag and drop numbers and symbols to re-order them

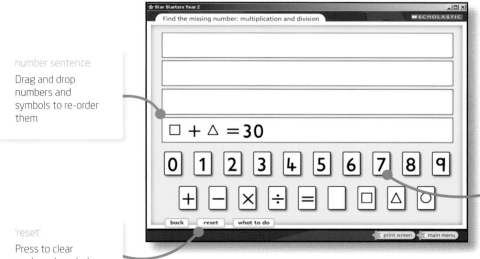

numbers and symbols
Drag numbers and symbols onto a line to build a number sentence

'reset'
Press to clear cards and symbols from screen

Find the missing number: multiplication and division

Strand

Calculating

Learning objective

Use the symbols ×, ÷ and = to record and interpret number sentences; calculate the value of an unknown in a number sentence

Type of starter

Reason

Whiteboard tools

- Move cards and symbols onto the line to build a number sentence.
- Drag and drop numbers and symbols within a line to re-order them.
- Drag cards off the line to remove them.
- Press 'reset' to clear the cards and symbols from the screen and start again.

What to do

This activity encourages children to read number sentences as well as do the calculations. Create a multiplication sentence (for example, $2 \times \square = 10$) and then ask the children to read it out. Ask them for the answer to the calculation and then invite them to read the number sentence again, inserting the previously missing number. Initially, use multiplication sentences in the 2- and 5-times tables and prepare number sentences with just one element missing, such as $\triangle \times 5 = 20$. Then move on to related division facts and examples in which two symbols are used to stand for unknown numbers (for example, $\square \times \triangle = 20$).

Differentiation

Less confident: check that the children understand the meaning of the symbols before starting the activity. Limit the number range to multiplication facts in the 2-times table initially so that children start to recognise a pattern of answers.

More confident: ask the children to make up their own number sentences on the whiteboard and read these out. Challenge the whole class to calculate the answer.

Key questions

- *Can you read this number sentence?*
- *What number could this symbol stand for? What other numbers could it be?*

numbers sentence
Drag numbers and symbols to re-order them

'reset'
Press to clear cards and symbols from screen

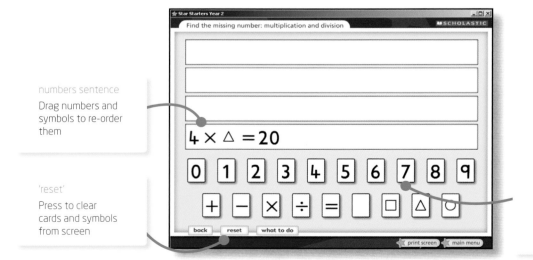

numbers and symbols
Drag and drop onto a line to build a number sentence

Dominoes: names of shapes

Strand

Understanding shape

Learning objective

Identify shapes from pictures of them

Type of starter

Recall

Whiteboard tools

- Press 'new' to start a new game.
- Press the 'miss a go' button to take another domino from the pot.
- Dominoes:
  - Drag and drop into the game
  - Press to rotate 90°.
- Press 'winner' if Player 1 or Player 2 has placed all of the dominoes.

What to do

The aim of this game is to assess children's understanding and recall of the common 2D shapes and to help them further to visualise the shapes by matching the names to shapes. The game is played in the same way as standard dominoes, with two players or groups playing against each other. Each player (or team) is dealt four dominoes, with the others left in a central pot. A starter domino is selected by the computer to begin the game, and the players then take turns to play. If you are placing the dominoes for the children, make sure at all times that the children use correct mathematical vocabulary to describe the shapes they wish to place.

If a player is unable to place a domino, they should press 'miss a go' and take one from the central pot. The game continues until a player places all of their dominoes, and is declared the winner, or there are no more dominoes left in the pot. If a stalemate situation occurs - in which neither player is able to put down a domino and the pot is empty - the player with fewest remaining dominoes is the winner. Encourage the children to describe the shapes on each domino before placing it.

Differentiation

Less confident: let the children use talk partners to discuss moves, which will help to boost confidence and affirm their decisions. Provide some flat shapes to further support their understanding.
More confident: play 'beat the teacher', in which children pit themselves against an adult in the classroom.

Key questions

- Which shapes were easy to spot? Which were difficult?
- Which shape matches 'hexagon'?
- Can you find a domino shape with five corners and five sides? Where would you place it? What is its name?

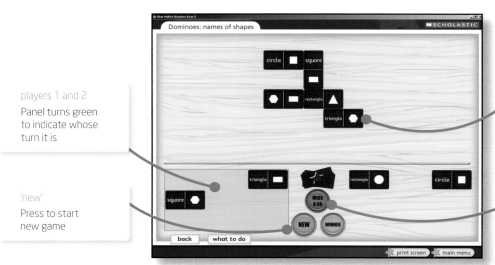

players 1 and 2
Panel turns green to indicate whose turn it is

'new'
Press to start new game

domino
- Drag domino to playing space
- Rotate by pressing top right-hand corner

'miss a go'
Press to take another domino from the pot

Reflection patterns

Strand

Understanding shape

Learning objective

Identify reflective symmetry in patterns

Type of starter

Refine

Whiteboard tools
- Use 'options' to select the following: squares on side: 6; mirror line: vertical.
- Press individual squares on the left-hand side of the grid to build a pattern.
- Press 'done' when you have completed the pattern.
- Press on individual squares on the right-hand side of the grid to build the reflection of the pattern.
- Press the white square, then press any coloured squares on the grid to clear them.
- Press 'reset' to clear grid and start again.

What to do

Using two colours, create a vertical pattern on the left-hand side of the grid, one square away from the reflection line. Ask the class to tell you what the reflection would look like and where each colour would be if the pattern were reflected in the vertical line. Demonstrate the reflection by using a mirror before showing the image on the whiteboard. Repeat the activity with a different pattern, extending the grid to 10 × 10 squares (use the 'options' button to change the grid size). Move on to use the grid like a virtual 'pegboard' making a range of simple symmetrical patterns. Invite volunteers to come to the board to build up the reflections you have created.

Differentiation

Less confident: use the 6 × 6 grid and one colour only to familiarise the children with finding and describing the reflection. Provide squared paper to help them to build the pattern away from the board.
More confident: use two colours and the 10 × 10 grid to build a more complex 'pegboard' pattern to extend the children's thinking skills.

Key questions
- *Can you describe your pattern so that your partner can draw its reflection?*
- *How do you know that the other 'half' of the pattern is symmetrical? How can you check?*

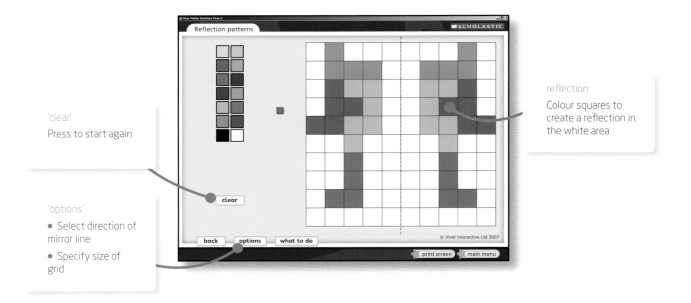

'clear'
Press to start again

'options'
- Select direction of mirror line
- Specify size of grid

reflection
Colour squares to create a reflection in the white area

Maps and directions

Strand

Understanding shape

Learning objective

Follow and give instructions involving position, direction and movement

Type of starter

Read

Whiteboard tools

- Drag and drop the direction and movement cards to prepare the route. Press 'move' to confirm the chosen route.
- Press 'show route' to display the directions selected so far.
- View the box at the top of the screen to identify which items the knight has collected along the route.

What to do

This activity develops children's understanding of position and movement. From a given starting point, ask the children for directions to guide the knight through the castle, using the direction and movement cards on the screen as prompts. The knight has to collect his sword, shield and helmet before making his way to the exit. Drag and drop each card into place to build up the route. The order in which the cards are placed affects whether the knight turns first or moves first. Press 'move' after each selection.

More than one route is available and some routes include barriers - so the quickest route is not necessarily the best. The position of the items and barriers changes randomly with each game. Press the 'show route' button to check the knight's progress. Encourage the children to check and challenge the route at this stage and start again if necessary. Make sure at all times that the children use the correct mathematical vocabulary when selecting an instruction from the screen, and use other vocabulary where appropriate (for example: *Turn clockwise towards the tent*).

Differentiation

Less confident: provide copies of the 'Maps and directions' photocopiable sheet on page 46 as additional support.

More confident: ask the children for alternative ways of giving the same directions (for example, using words such as *clockwise* or *anticlockwise*), or introducing the compass directions.

Key questions

- *What is the quickest way to move the knight to his sword? Out of the castle?*
- *Are there any other ways of moving from this point to this point?*

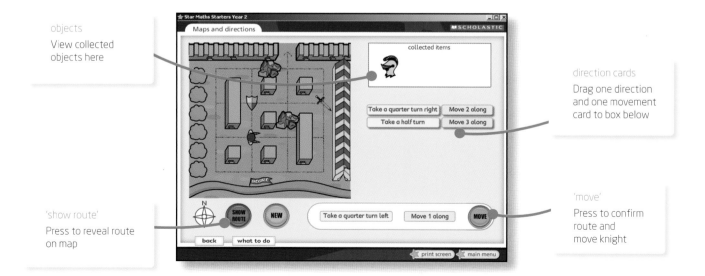

objects
View collected objects here

direction cards
Drag one direction and one movement card to box below

'show route'
Press to reveal route on map

'move'
Press to confirm route and move knight

Weighing scales: standard units

Strand

Measuring

Learning objective

Use standard units of weight

Type of starter

Rehearse

Whiteboard tools

● Drag and drop items on the left of the screen into the pan.
● Turn the digital readout on or off, as required.
● Select 'options' to make changes to the face of the scales, such as removing the numbers, or altering the number of subdivisions.

What to do

The aim of this activity is for the children to compare the weights of different items and to predict which items are heavier or lighter than one kilogram. First, select two items and ask: *Which is heavier? Which is lighter?* Next, invite a child to choose an item from the screen that weighs more or less than another object on the screen that you have selected. Ask: *Will there be a big difference between these two weights? What objects do you think would weigh nearly the same?* Test the children's predictions by dragging and dropping the items onto the scales. Either in this session or in subsequent sessions, set the question: *Which items weigh more than one kilogram?*

Differentiation

Less confident: give the children a range of standard classroom resources, ranging from books to pencils and glue sticks. Tell them to put the objects in order, from heaviest to lightest. Ask: *Are there any clues to whether an object is heavy or light?* (For example, what they are made from, the size of the object and so on.)
More confident: ask the children to read out the weights and to write down their answers. Then instruct them to begin grouping some of the objects that have similar weights. Challenge the children to identify five items round the classroom that weigh more than 1 kilogram.

Key questions

● *Which object is heavier/lighter?*
● *Which objects weigh more than one kilogram?*
● *Approximately how many loaves of bread will weigh the same as the bag of flour?*

items
Drag food items onto the scales

'options'
Set maximum weight, subdivision, and whether or not to show numbers on analogue scale

scales pan
Add or remove items by dragging them on or off the pan

digital readout
Can be turned on or off to reveal exact weight of items

Measuring jug: read a scale

Strand

Measuring

Learning objective

Read the numbered divisions on a scale and interpret the divisions between them

Type of starter

Read

Whiteboard tools
- Press the 'options' button to set the following: set 'scale' to 1000; 'scale mode' to full; 'subdivisions' to none; 'fill steps' to manual.
- Press 'in' to fill the jug, and press it again to stop filling.
- Press 'out' to empty the jug, and press it again to stop emptying.
- Press 'reset' to start again.

What to do

Ask the children to read aloud together the divisions shown on the measuring jug from 100ml to 1000ml, as you point to them. Then tell the children that they are going to find out how much water has been put in the jug by reading the markers on it. Fill the jug part way up to a certain level (for example, the 300ml mark) and explain that the level is read to the nearest marker. Then discuss with the children what they think the reading is. Next, ask them about readings between the markers (for example, 50ml) and repeat the earlier activities. Encourage the children to describe the levels using millilitres and litres (for example: *about half a litre; the jug holds one litre or 1000 millilitres*).

Differentiation

Less confident: in the early stages, focus the children's attention on reading the scale accurately.
More confident: fill then partially empty the jug and ask the children to find the difference between the two capacities.

Key questions

- *The contents of a bottle of water have been poured into this jug. How much water was there in the bottle?*
- *If the contents of another bottle of water is added, what level will the water reach in the jug?*

'reset'
Press to start again

'options'
Select following options:
- scale: 1000ml
- scale mode: full
- subdivisions: none
- fill steps: manual

'in'
Press to fill jug; press again to stop filling

'out'
Press to empty the jug; press again to stop emptying

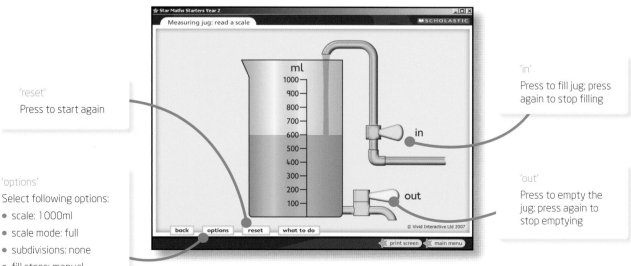

Fixing points (ITP): using a ruler

Strand

Measuring

Learning objective

Use a ruler to draw and measure lines to the nearest centimetre

Type of starter

Refine

Whiteboard tools
- Press 'grid size' to change the size of the grid.
- Press any two points on the grid to create a line between them.
- Drag one end of the line to another grid point to draw lines of different lengths more quickly.
- Press the 'ruler' button to show or hide the ruler at the bottom of the screen.
- Use the blue circle at one end of the ruler to rotate it and drag it into the correct position for measurement.
- Press 'reset' to remove any lines.

What to do

The aim of this activity is to help the children refine their skills in reading scales; it also provides a good demonstration of how to use a ruler. The program opens as a blank grid: pressing on a series of dots will allow you to create lines of different lengths very quickly and accurately. Press the 'ruler' button to launch it. If only horizontal and vertical lines are used for measuring, then the lengths will always be an exact number of centimetres. Once you have got used to the program, you can change the size of the grid if you wish.

Differentiation

Less confident: limit the activity to measuring horizontal lines and ask the children to measure to the nearest centimetre.
More confident: use vertical and diagonal lines and ask the children to measure more accurately to the nearest half centimetre.

Key questions
- *At what point should the ruler be positioned when measuring? For example, should the end of the line be at the end of the ruler, at zero or at 1?*
- *How would you write down the measurement that is half way between 3cm and 4cm?*
- *What in the classroom is about 4cm long?*

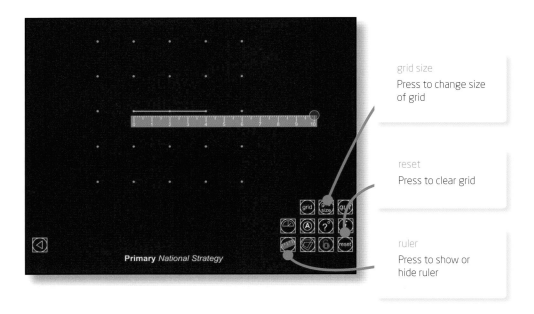

grid size
Press to change size of grid

reset
Press to clear grid

ruler
Press to show or hide ruler

Clocks: read the time

Strand

Measuring

Learning objective

Read the time to the quarter hour

Type of starter

Read

Whiteboard tools
● Press the 'randomise' button to select a random analogue time.
● Drag the clock hands manually to move the time on the analogue clock.
● Use the 'options' button to specify the settings for the 'randomise' functions. You can also choose to link the hour and minutes hands on the analogue clock.

What to do

This starter helps children to read accurately the time on an analogue clock face to the nearest quarter hour. Move the clock hands by pressing and dragging them round, in the same way as with a standard classroom clock. Display a time set to the hour (such as 3 o'clock), and ask the children to role play asking for and reading the time to each other. Select another time on the hour. In subsequent sessions, ask one of the children to set the time for the others to read.

Once the children are confident with reading time to the hour and half hour, introduce quarter-hour times. (Note that if you have selected to 'link hands', when the minute hand is moved to 3, the hour hand will automatically move on a quarter-hour increment.) Repeat with different times. Use the 'randomise' button to vary between times to the hour, half hour and quarter hour.

Differentiation

Less confident: reinforce hourly time, using real-life examples. (For example: *School starts at nine o'clock.*)
More confident: ask the children for other important times during their day, such as: *I go to bed at quarter past eight; school starts at 8.45.* Encourage them to show these on the clock face.

Key questions

● *What are the important times of the day?* (For example, mealtimes, schooltimes and bedtimes.)
● *What happens to the hour hand as we change the minute hand? Why is it moving and where is it moving towards?*

'options'
Press and select the analogue settings you require

'randomise'
Press to select a random analogue time

hands on analogue clock
Drag the hands to alter the time as you wish

Block graph: favourite fruit

Strand

Handling data

Learning objective

Represent data using block graphs to show results

Type of starter

Refresh

Whiteboard tools
- Type in the title of the chart and labels for the categories.
- Select the squares to record an entry.
- Press the 'options' button to extend or change the scale of the block graph.

What to do
Prepare the chart title 'Our favourite fruit' and write in popular types of fruit in the 'enter label' text boxes. Next, ask the children to tell you their favourite fruit. (It is unlikely to be necessary, but the vertical scale on the graph can be extended up to 20 using the 'options' button.) Build the block graph as the children vote for their favourites. Ask them to hold up their hands for each category or to come to the board to place a block on the graph. Ask some simple questions about the data (see 'Key questions' below for examples).

Differentiation
Less confident: show the children the numbers on the vertical scale representing each fruit and ask them, for example: *How many children like apples best?* Encourage them to count the blocks to check their answers.
More confident: challenge the children to make some statements about the class's favourite fruit from the results shown on the graph.

Key questions
- *What is the favourite type of fruit? How do you know?*
- *How many children like apples best? How many like bananas best?*
- *How many more children prefer apples to pears?*

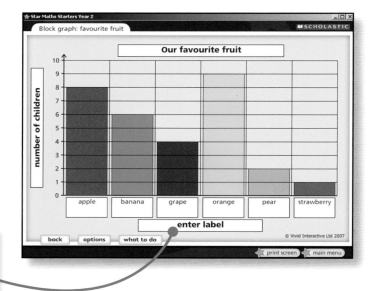

labels
Use keyboard to type in fruit labels

Targets

◼ Find the target numbers using the cards below.

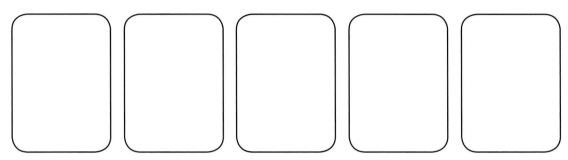

◼ How I worked out the target answer.

_____

_____

_____

_____

_____

_____

_____

_____

Bingo

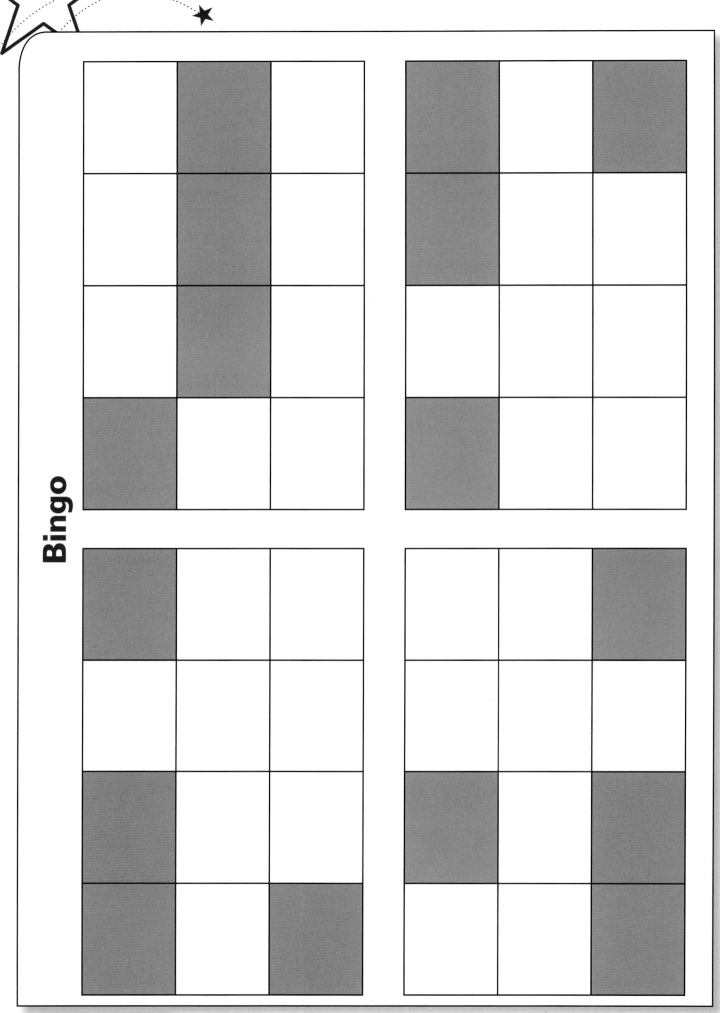

Star Maths Starters ★ Year 2
PHOTOCOPIABLE

Beanstalk

Maps and directions

■ Plan your route using the map below.

Moves

_____

_____

_____

_____

_____

_____

_____

Teacher's name _____

Maths Star Starters diary page

Name of Star Starter	PNS objectives covered	How was activity used	Date activity was used

Also available in this series:

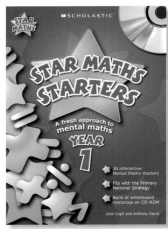
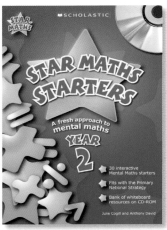
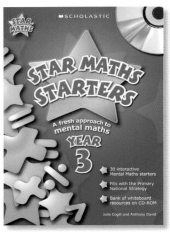
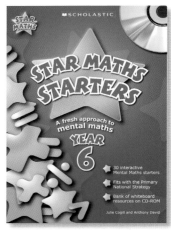

ISBN 978-1407-10007-4   ISBN 978-1407-10008-1   ISBN 978-1407-10009-8

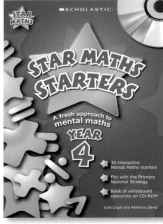

ISBN 978-1407-10010-4   ISBN 978-1407-10011-1   ISBN 978-1407-10012-8

ISBN 978-1407-10031-9 ISBN 978-1407-10032-6 ISBN 978-1407-10033-3 ISBN 978-1407-10034-0 ISBN 978-1407-10035-7 ISBN 978-1407-10036-4

To find out more, call: 0845 603 9091
or visit our website www.scholastic.co.uk